HER MAJESTY'S
INSPECTORATE OF POLLUTION

Environmental Protection Act 1990

Technical Guidance Note (Monitoring)

M1

Sampling Facility Requirements for the Monitoring of Particulates in Gaseous Releases to Atmosphere

January 1993

London : H M S O

Second impression 1995

ISBN 0 11 752777 7

Prepared for publication by Technical Guidance Branch
Her Majesty's Inspectorate of Pollution

Her Majesty's Inspectorate of Pollution

HMIP, currently part of the Department of the Environment, has a key role in protecting and improving Britain's environment. HMIP's responsibilities were increased by the 1990 *Environmental Protection Act*, and it now regulates 200 categories of industry, 5000 major industrial plants and 8000 premises using or storing radioactive material.

Enquiries about the contents of this publication should be made to:

HMIP
Technical Guidance Branch
Government Buildings
Burghill Road
Westbury-on-Trym
Bristol BS10 6EZ

Telephone: 0117 987 3253

Contents

1.0 Introduction

1.1 This Note is issued by Her Majesty's Inspectorate of Pollution as guidance to Inspectors. It is one of a series providing information on technical subjects relevant to HMIP's regulatory functions, and will be of interest to other regulatory bodies. This Note provides technical information on monitoring, and is intended for the Inspectorate's monitoring contractors, industry and any other interested parties, as guidance on the technical information used by regulators when carrying out their duties.

1.2 This Note and diagrams are issued as guidance to those providing the facilities for, or undertaking, the determination of the particulate content of gas streams flowing in chimneys or enclosed ducts to the requirements of *BS 3405:1983 British Standard Method for measurement of particulate emission including grit and dust (simplified method).* Although this information refers specifically to the BCURA (British Coal Utilisation Research Association) sampling equipment, the requirements apply in principle to the other available apparatus assemblies mentioned in the British Standard.

1.3 In order to measure quantitatively the mass of particulate present in such gas streams, it is necessary to withdraw, isokinetically, samples of the gases flowing in the chimney or duct at a suitable sample plane, which may often be at a remote location and require the provision of a sample platform and dedicated access. It is essential to read these notes in conjunction with *BS 3405:1983.*

2.0 Sample Plane Selection

2.1 Before considering the installation of sample access holes and associated sampling facilities on a duct or chimney, it is important to confirm that a suitable sample plane location exists for sampling, particularly with respect to the gas flow profile in the duct or chimney. An exploratory pitot-static tube survey, of the duct gas velocity pressure profile, should be undertaken along the full length of the proposed sample lines, at the proposed sample plane. For metal or other thin-walled ducts or chimneys, 13mm (half inch) diameter pilot holes, drilled through the flue wall on the centres of the proposed sample access holes, will enable a small bore pitot-static tube of suitable length to be used for this purpose.

NB For circular ducts, two "pilot" holes at 90° to each other on the circumference of the sample plane will normally be satisfactory. See **Figures 1A and 1B**.

For square or rectangular ducts a "number" of pilot holes are required, located in the same duct wall and spaced at intervals, so as to provide sample traverse lines along the centre of equal areas of duct cross-section in the sample plane. See **Figures 2A and 2B.**

2.2 Then, if the initial choice of sample plane location proves unsuitable, an alternative position can be examined without incurring excessive cost.

Figure 1A Circular duct - four point sampling

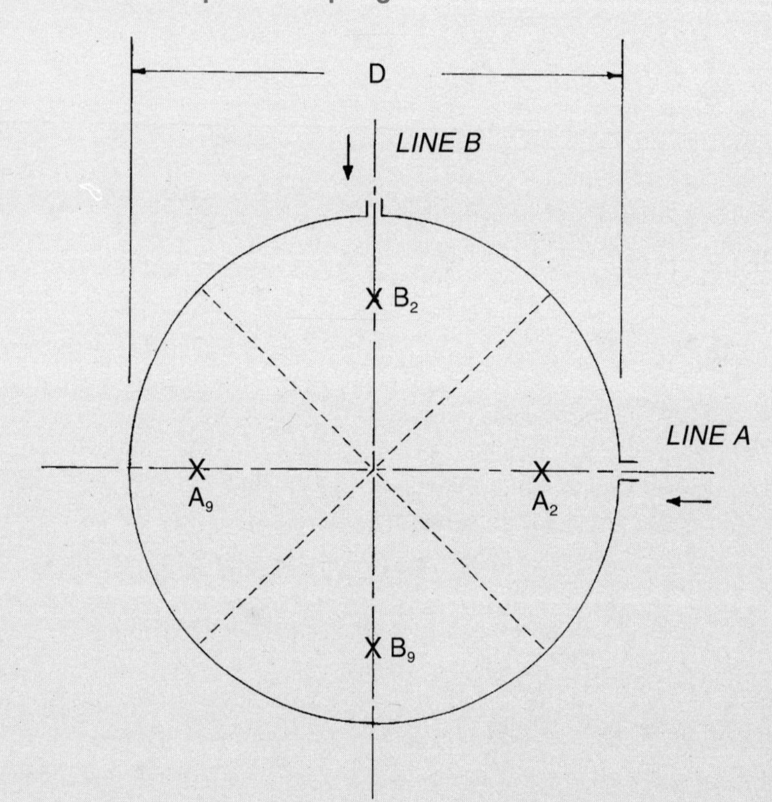

The cross-sectional area of duct relative to each sample point is shown enclosed by dotted lines.

Pitot traverse point	1	2	3	4	5	6	7	8	9	10
Location on duct diameter (D)	0.05D	0.15D	0.25D	0.35D	0.45D	0.55D	0.65D	0.75D	0.85D	0.95D
Sample point location		X							X	

Figure 1B Circular duct - eight point sampling

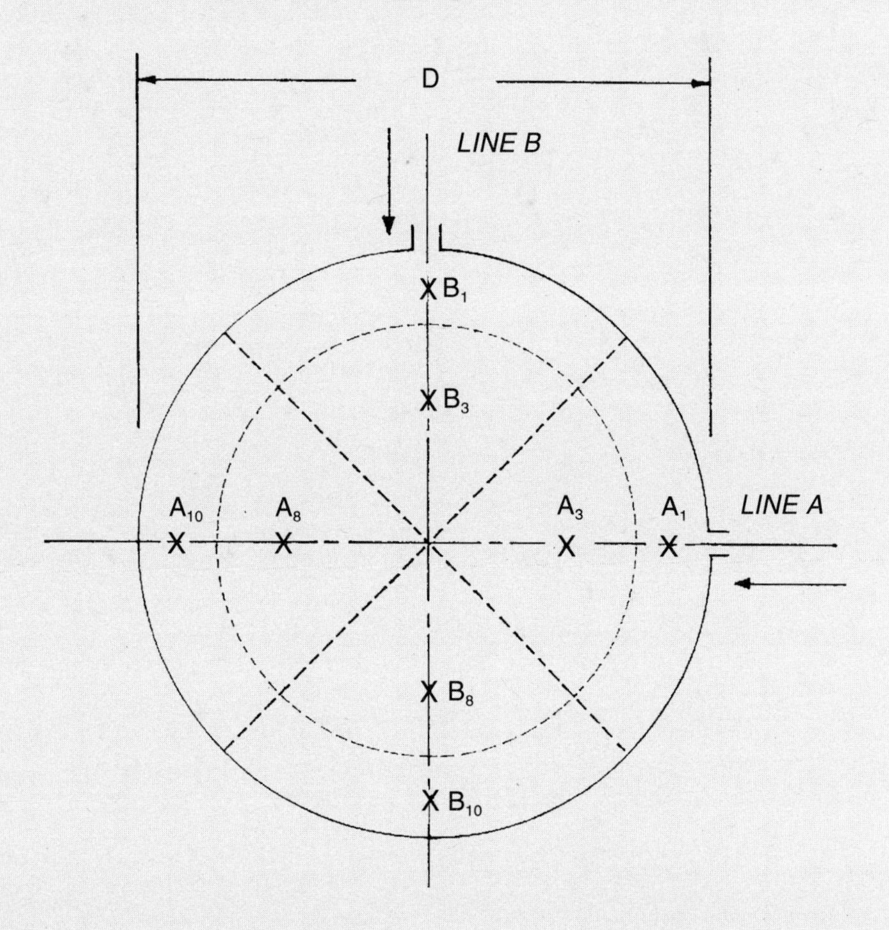

The cross-sectional area of duct relative to each sample point is shown enclosed by dotted lines.

Pitot traverse point	1	2	3	4	5	6	7	8	9	10
Location on duct diameter (D)	0.065D	0.15D	0.25D	0.35D	0.45D	0.55D	0.65D	0.75D	0.85D	0.935D
Sample point location	X		X					X		X

2.3 On ducts of very large cross-section, (eg. above 2.5m sample traverse depth), it may be preferable to undertake pitot-static tube and sample probe traverses from both ends of each sample line, through properly located sample access fitments, to avoid the difficulties inherent in using very long sample probes, say above 3m in length. See **Figures 3A, 3B and 3C.** Such a situation should be carefully evaluated during the procedures undertaken, to identify a suitable sample plane, and also identify any restriction on the use of long probes due to the presence of adjacent structures.

2.4 It may not be possible, however, to undertake the same investigatory procedures on brick or other thick walled or lined ducts or chimneys, when selecting a suitable sample plane, due to the engineering problems involved. In these circumstances, the advice of professionals experienced in the practice of isokinetic sampling may be used, in order to try and avoid costly errors in making sample plane selection in these difficult situations.

General guidance on the selection of suitable sample planes is provided in *BS 3405: 1983* (sections 6.3.1 and 6.3.2, Figure 3 and Appendix F of that Standard).

Figure 2A Square/rectangular duct - four point sampling

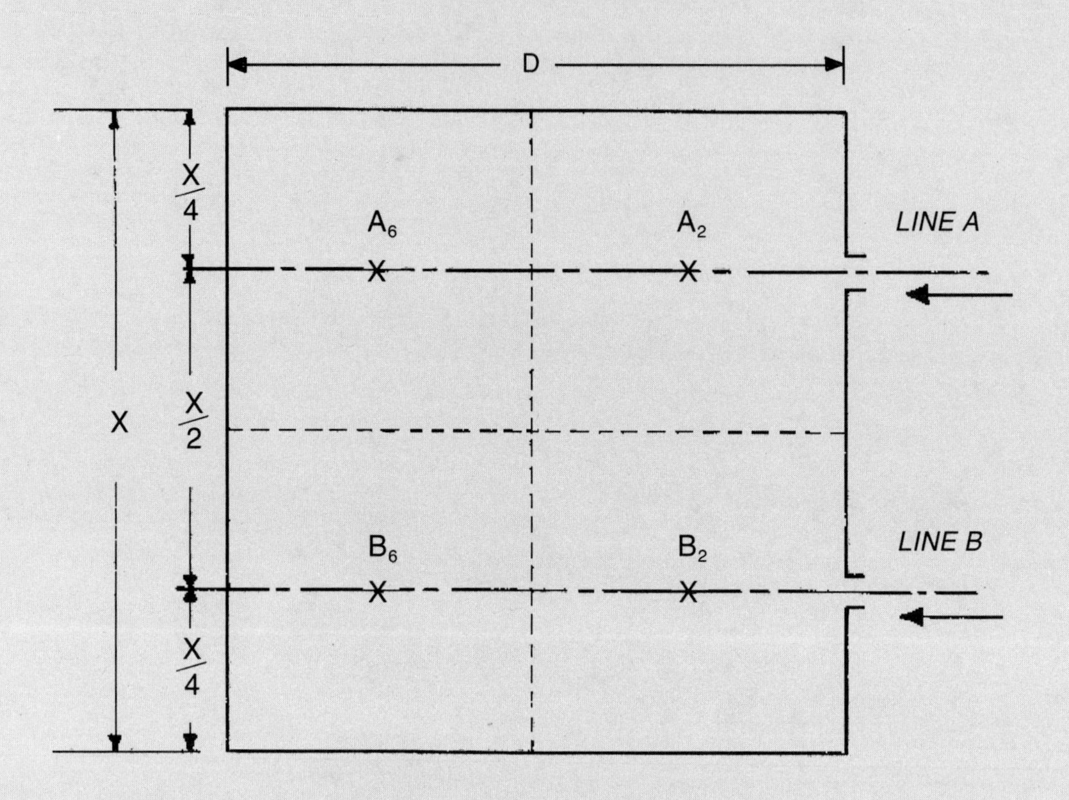

The duct traverse dimension (D) is defined as the internal distance between the duct walls at the sample plane.

The cross-sectional area of duct relative to each sample point is shown enclosed by dotted lines.

Pitot traverse point	1	2	3	4	5	6	7
Location on duct traverse dimension (D)	0.125D	0.25D	0.375D	0.5D	0.625D	0.75D	0.875D
Sample point location		X				X	

NB The minimum number of sample points that should be used on each pitot-static tube sample traverse are shown in the table. See also Figure 2B.

Figure 2B Square/rectangular duct - eight point sampling

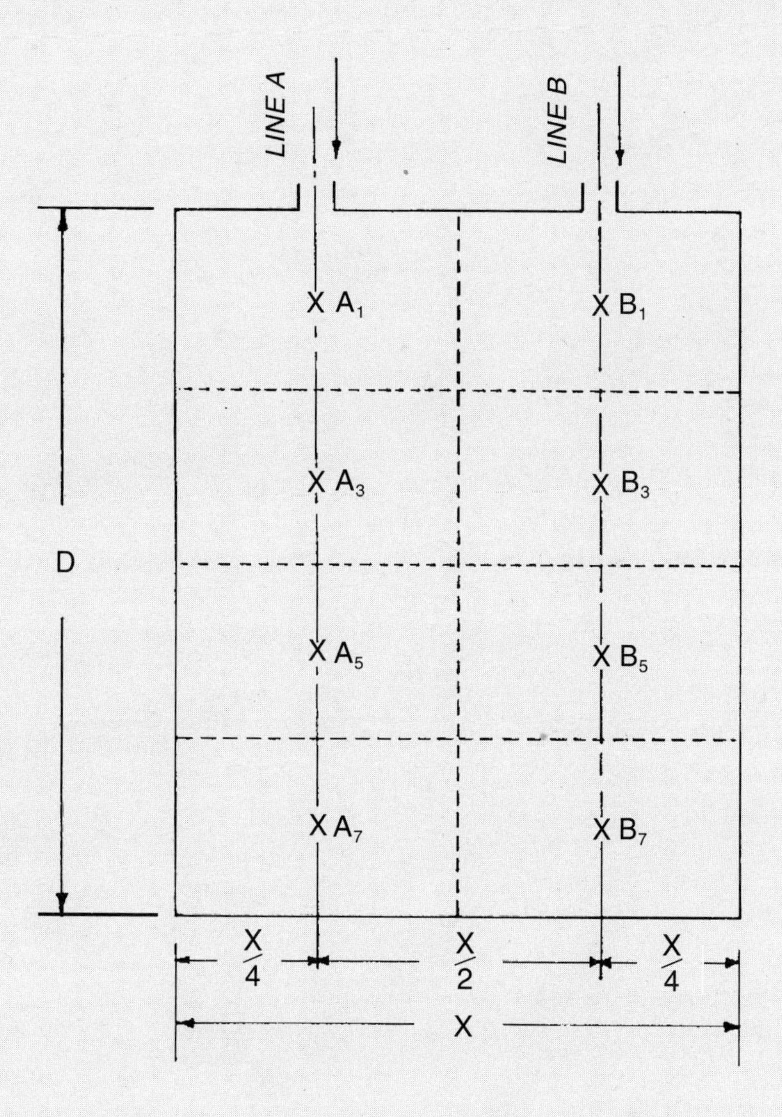

The duct traverse dimension (D) is defined as the internal distance between the duct walls at the sample plane.

The cross-sectional area of duct relative to each sample point is shown enclosed by dotted lines.

Pitot traverse point	1	2	3	4	5	6	7
Location on duct traverse dimension (D)	0.125D	0.25D	0.375D	0.5D	0.625D	0.75D	0.875D
Sample point location	X		X		X		X

NB The minimum number of sample points that should be used on each pitot-static tube sample traverse are shown in the table.

In the case of ducts of large cross-section or where the gas flow profile is not uniform, further additional pitot-static tube measurements should be undertaken at the intermediate positions to those tabulated. See also Figure 2A.

Figure 3A Typical arrangement of access fitments on large circular ducts

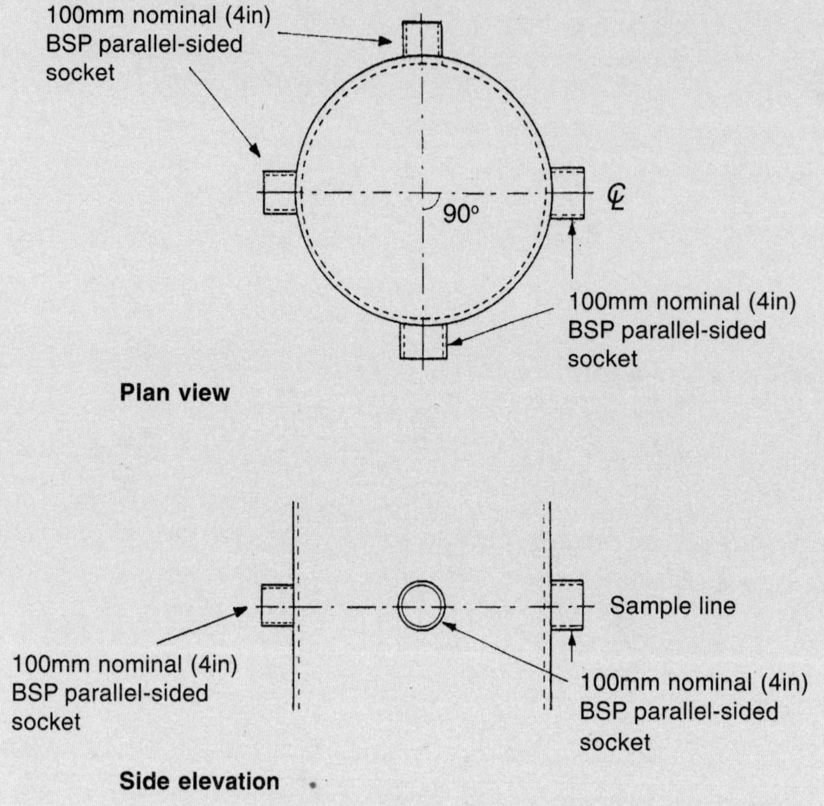

100mm nominal (4in) BSP parallel-sided socket

90°

℄

100mm nominal (4in) BSP parallel-sided socket

Plan view

Sample line

100mm nominal (4in) BSP parallel-sided socket

100mm nominal (4in) BSP parallel-sided socket

Side elevation

Figure 3B Typical arrangement of access fitments on large square/rectangular ducts

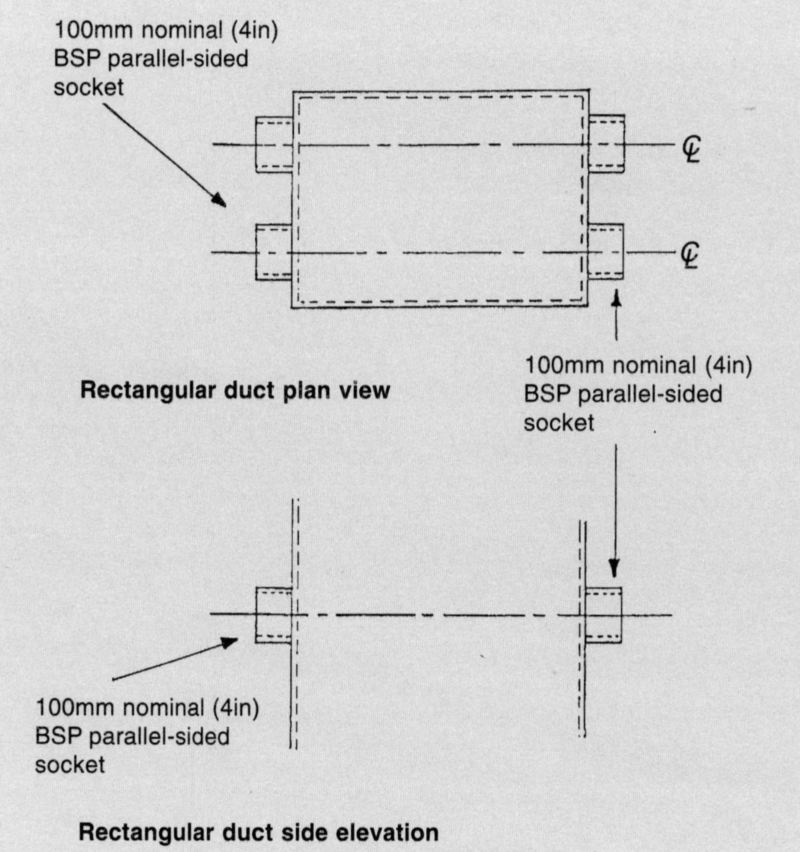

Figure 3C Typical area requirement behind probe for handling

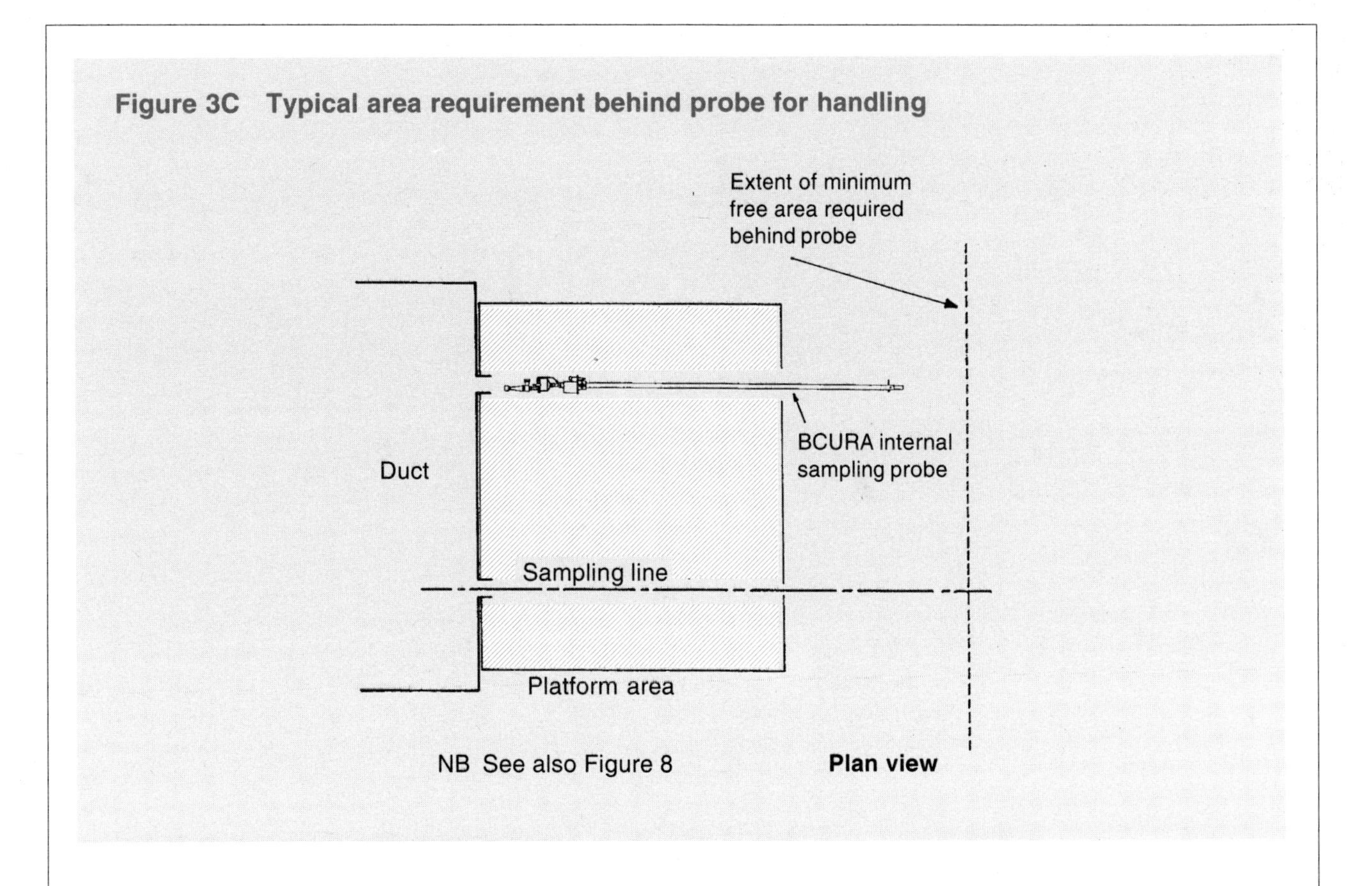

3.0 Sample Points

3.1 Following acceptance of the sample plane location, each sample hole access to each sample line should be fitted with a 100mm nominal (4in) BSP parallel-sided socket, minimum internal diameter above the threads 110mm, made from material compatible with the duct wall. When not in use for sampling, each fitment should be sealed with a suitable 100mm nominal (4in) BSP plug.

NB 100mm nominal (4in) BSP parallel-sided sockets are designed to fit over 100mm nominal bore pipe and are 110mm diameter above the threads. Great care is necessary during the installation of the sockets on to the duct/ chimney, to ensure that weld flash or other obstructions do not intrude within the minimum clear diameter of 110mm through the duct wall. See **Figures 4A, 4B and 4C.**

(On a practical level the protection of the sealing plug and access fitment socket threads from any corrosive effects will:

a. facilitate removal of the sealing plug when required;

b. more importantly, ensure that the probe holder retaining cam, on the BCURA sample probe holder, can be properly secured in the access fitment during the sampling exercise, to facilitate correct pitot-static tube/sample probe alignment).

3.2 Existing sample fitments on ducts or chimneys, made up from 125mm nominal (5in) bore pipe and flanged to the requirements of the appropriate section of *BS 4504: 1989*, should only continue to be used, providing that all the requirements for sampling and safety are satisfied. The replacement of such flanged 125mm nominal (5in) bore pipe fitments with conventional 100mm nominal (4in) diameter BSP sockets should be undertaken at the earliest convenient opportunity.

Figure 4A Sample access fitment - method of mounting to duct wall (including plug closure)

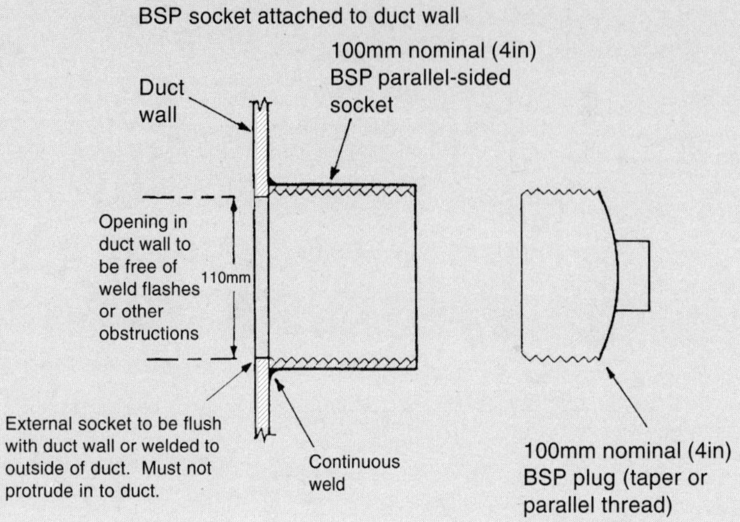

BSP socket attached to duct wall

Duct wall

100mm nominal (4in) BSP parallel-sided socket

Opening in duct wall to be free of weld flashes or other obstructions

110mm

External socket to be flush with duct wall or welded to outside of duct. Must not protrude in to duct.

Continuous weld

100mm nominal (4in) BSP plug (taper or parallel thread)

Figure 4B Sample access fitment - restriction in use due to presence of residual weld flash/ weld metal

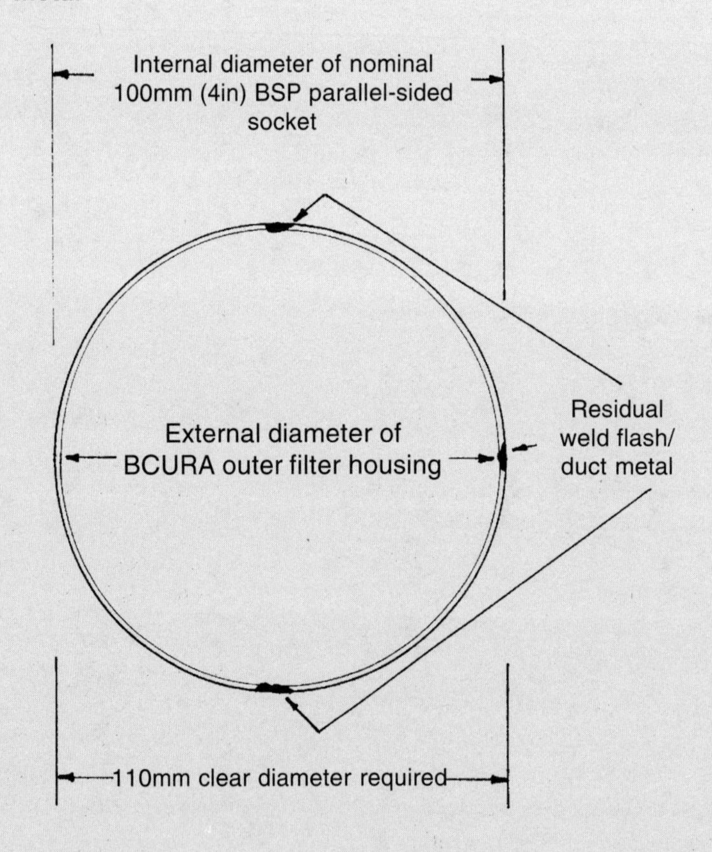

NB Any intrusion of weld flash/duct metal in to the full 110mm internal diameter of the nominal 100mm diameter (4in) BSP parallel-sided socket [used as sample access fitment] will prevent the free passage of the BCURA outer filter housing into the duct for sampling purposes. See also Figure 4C.

Figure 4C BCURA outer filter housing clearance within a nominal 100mm (4in) BSP parallel sided socket

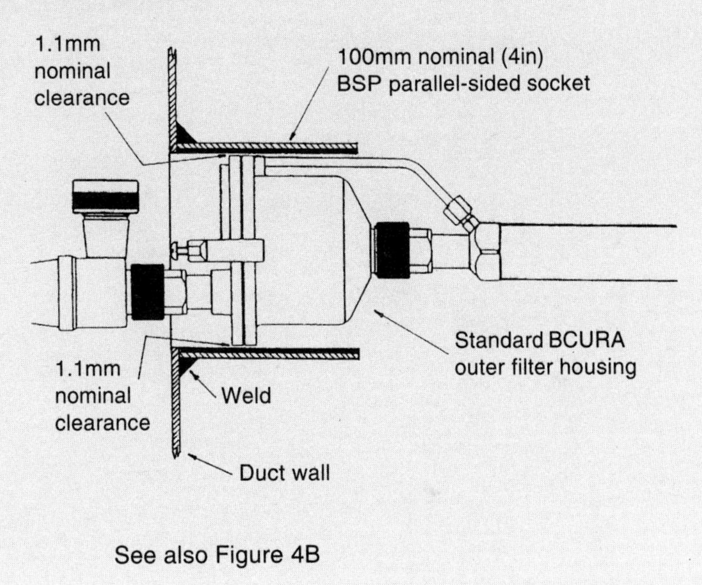

See also Figure 4B

3.3 When providing sampling facilities on circular ducts at or below 1016mm internal diameter, or in rectangular/square ducts at or below 610mm internal sample line depth, it will, in addition to the installation of the fitments described in 3.1 above, be necessary to fit recesses in the duct wall opposite each sample hole. This provision enables the BCURA equipment to be correctly located at the sampling position furthest from the sample hole on each sample line, under standard "four-point" sampling conditions. See **Figures 5A and 5B. (see also Graphs 1 and 2**).

Figure 5A Use of recesses on small circular ducts to permit location of BCURA probe nozzle at correct sample position - furthest from sample hole

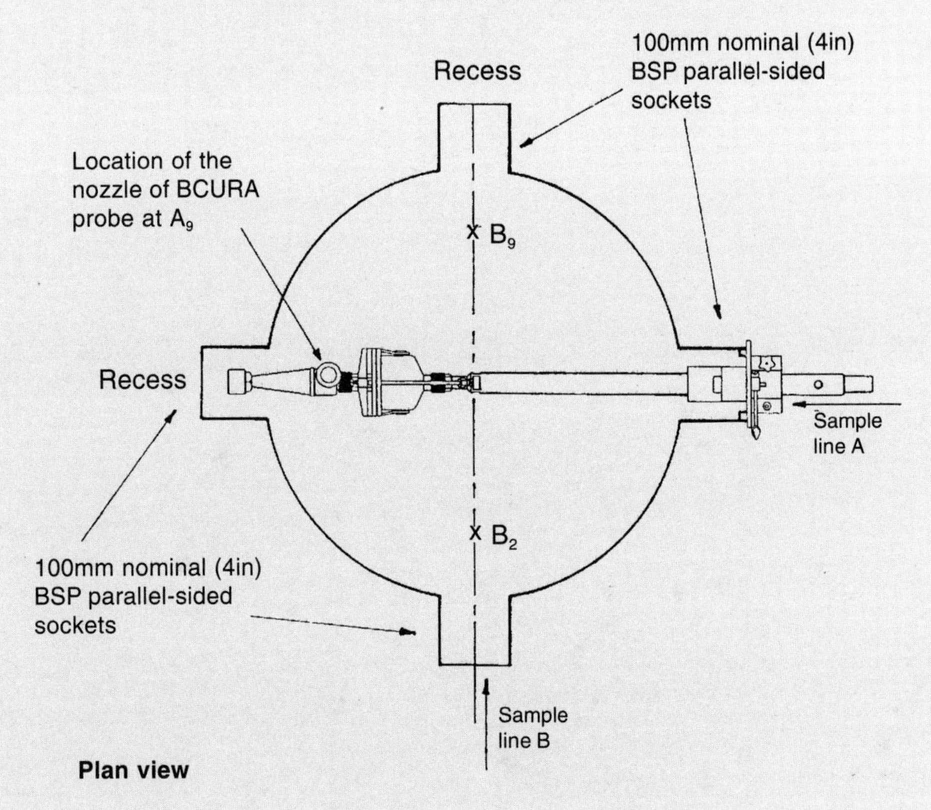

Figure 5B Use of recesses on small square/rectangular ducts to permit location of BCURA probe nozzle at correct sample position - furthest from sample hole

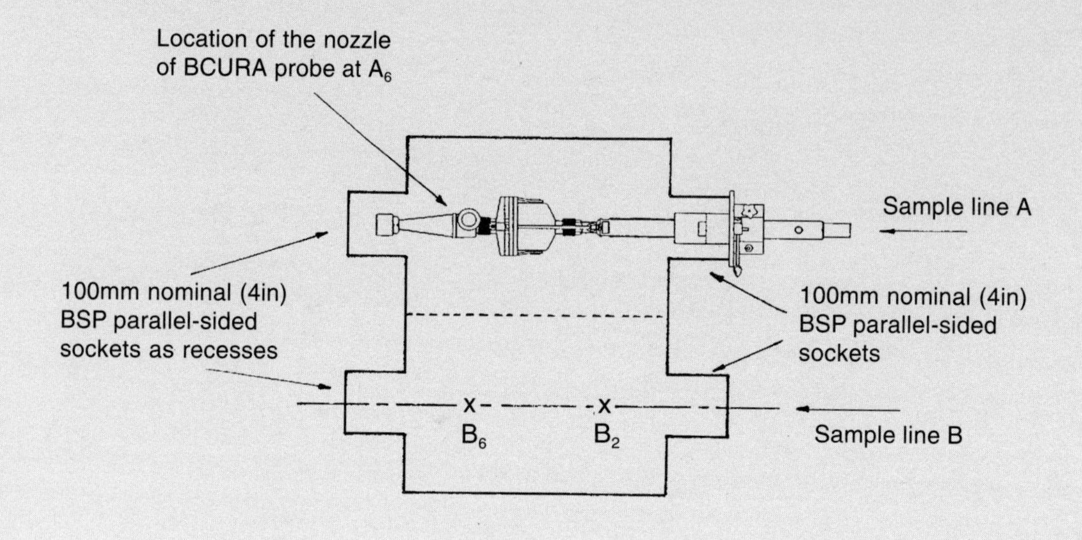

Plan view

Graph 1 Recesses required for square or rectangular ducts

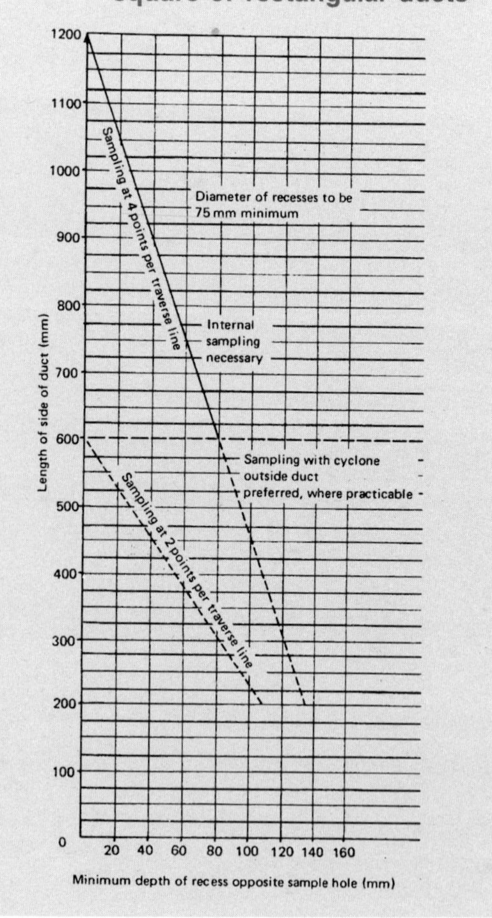

Graph 2 Recesses required for circular ducts

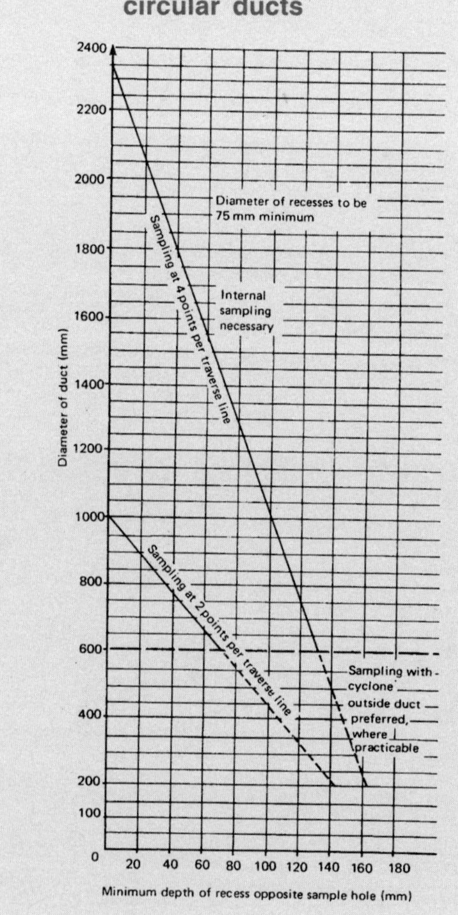

NB The recesses are produced most easily, by fitting standard 100mm nominal (4in) BSP parallel-sided sockets, as used for the sample point access fitments, in the duct wall directly opposite the sample points in the sample plane.

On these small sized ducts it will be necessary to employ either a foreshortened BCURA probe holder, or use a 125-100 nominal (5-4in) bell reducer over the 100mm nominal (4in) BSP socket, in order to locate correctly the sample probe at the sampling position nearest to the sample hole on each sample line, under standard four-point sampling. See **Figures 5C and 5D.**

Figure 5C Use of a foreshortened BCURA probe holder for small ducts

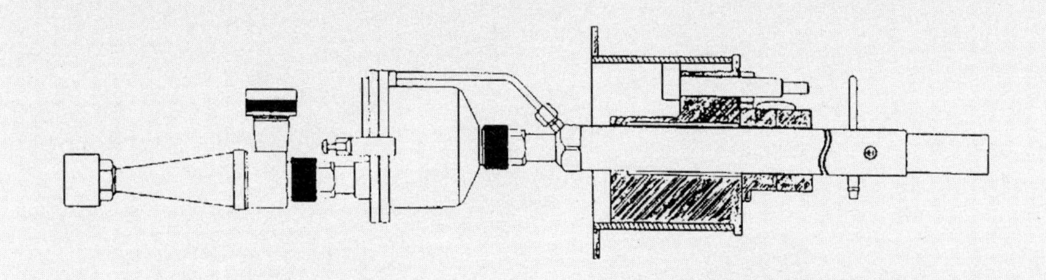

Figure 5C(i) Standard BCURA probe and holder in sample access fitment

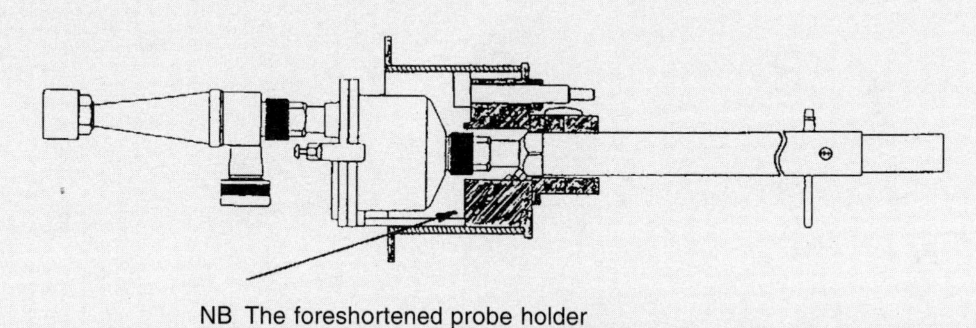

Figure 5C(ii) Standard BCURA probe holder and foreshortened holder in sample access fitment

3.4 Where it is known that standard "eight-point" sampling will be required, (due to gas flow conditions at the sample plane, because of the size of the duct or for some other reason), it will also be necessary to fit recesses in the duct wall opposite each sample hole in circular ducts at or below 2344 mm internal diameter, and in rectangular/square ducts at or below 1219mm internal sample line depth as outlined in 3.3 above. (See also **Graphs 1 and 2**).

Figure 5D Bell Reducer

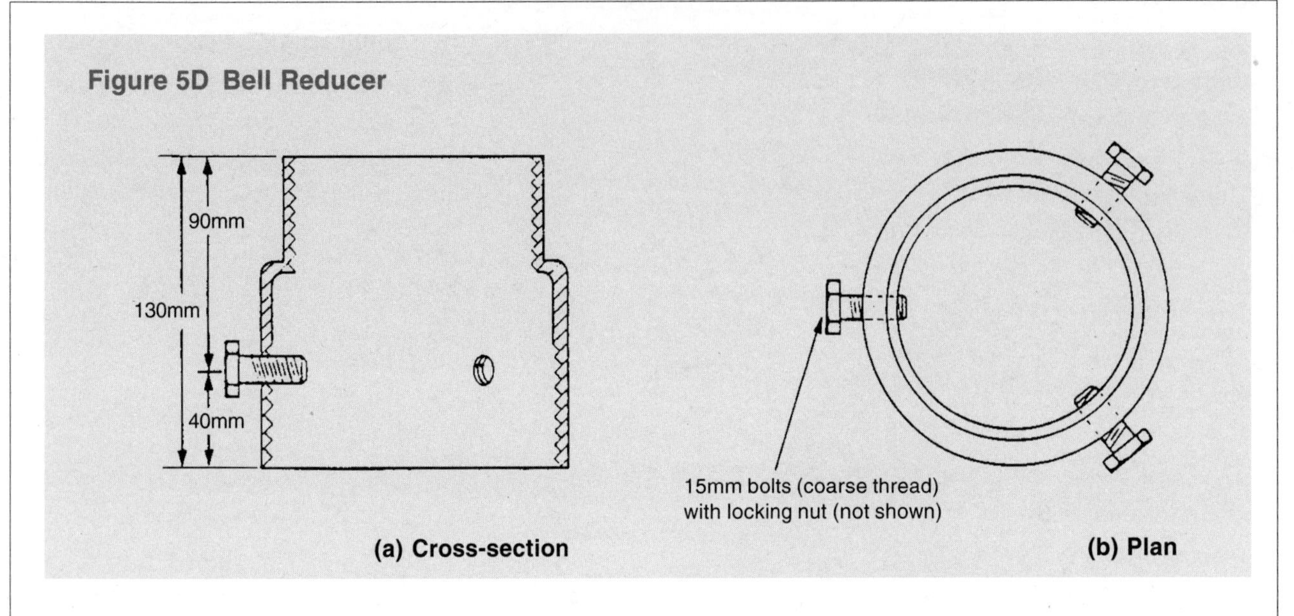

(a) Cross-section **(b) Plan**

3.5 On very small size ducts (ie. under about 600mm diameter or the equivalent 0.283m cross sectional area for square or rectangular ducts), where the insertion of sampling equipment of relatively large cross section, in relation to the area of duct for gas flow, would result in unacceptable disturbance to the gas flow, it may be necessary to employ "external" sample collection methods or equipment. These, in turn, may permit the use of smaller diameter access fitments in the duct/chimney wall. Under these circumstances, prior consultation with the technical staff responsible for using the sampling equipment is essential, before undertaking the provision of sampling facilities at the sample plane. See **Figures 6A and 6B.**

Figure 6A Limiting size of duct cross-sectional area when using the internal BCURA sampling probe

* Equivalent area of square/rectangular ducts is 0.283 m^2

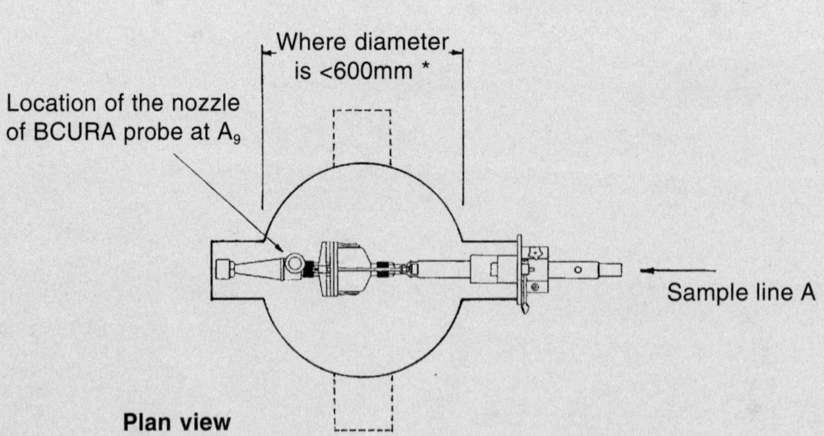

Plan view

NB Where a duct diameter is less than 600mm, the large cross-sectional area of the internal BCURA probe, relative to the full cross-sectional area of duct for gas flow, causes unacceptable disturbance to duct gas flow conditions. As an alternative, less bulky sampling equipment, such as for example, the external BCURA probe (see Figure 6B) should be used.

Figure 6B Typical application of the external BCURA sampling probe for small cross-sectional area ducts

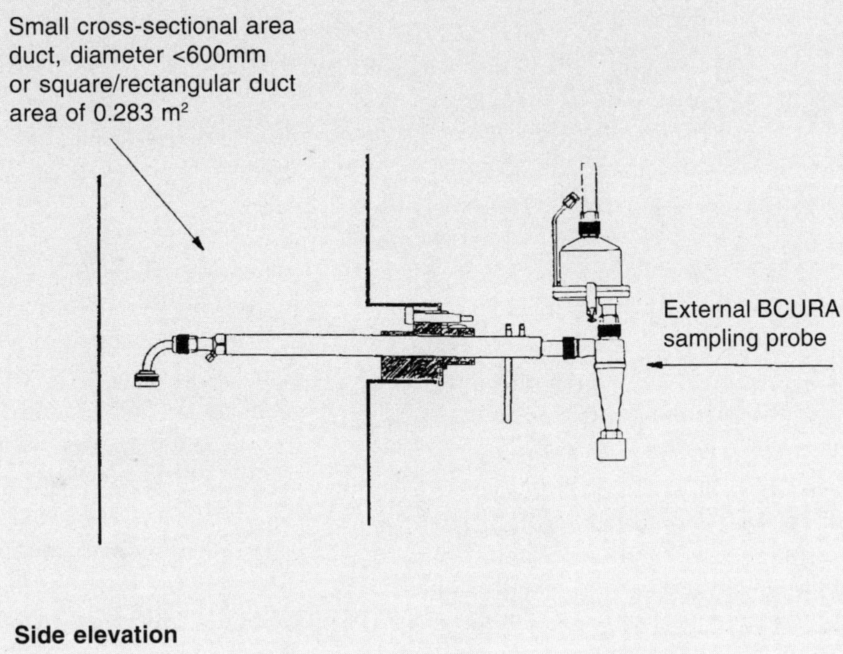

Small cross-sectional area duct, diameter <600mm or square/rectangular duct area of 0.283 m^2

External BCURA sampling probe

Side elevation

4.0 Sampling Platforms

4.1 The sampling platforms and platform access provided must be designed and constructed to satisfy the requirements of the current legislation. All such platforms and access must be maintained in good condition and repair, and be subject to regular mechanical inspection to confirm the integrity of the structures. In particular the provisions must include adequate and safe handrails, adequate and safe closure of all access ways on to and off the platform, and total enclosure of the platform floor area with a surround formed by a 230mm high continuous kick plate. The platform floor area should be free-draining. The platform should be designed and positioned so that the top of the handrail is about 125mm below the centre of the sample holes. See **Figure 7**. On remote platform locations it may be necessary for lifting facilities to be provided, to ensure that equipment can be safely transported to and from the platform. The provision and use of any lifting equipment will be required to conform with the current legislation.

Figure 7 Platform handrail / sample probe clearance requirements

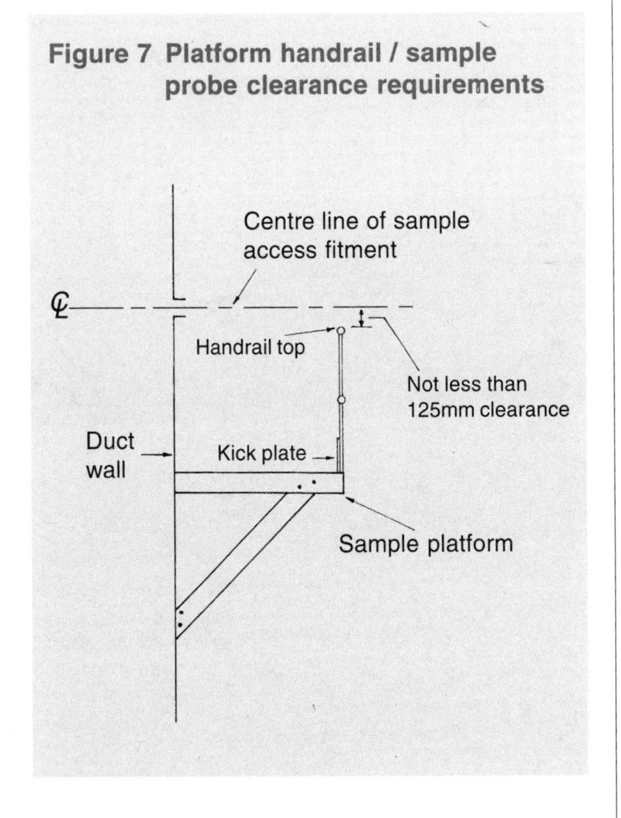

A selected bibliography of British Standards, guidance notes, advice and some current legislation is provided for reference as an Appendix, when the installation of sampling platforms and platform access is being considered.

NB The use of the top surfaces of arrestment equipment, such as bag filter housing, disengagement vessels and any associated ductwork, as a means of providing working area access to sample planes should be avoided, unless specifically constructed to the above requirements. There must be adequate level space free of obstructions or tripping hazards, and the floor must be free from risk of sudden metal failure due to unmonitored corrosive effects.

4.2 Sampling platforms should generally have a minimum working area of not less than $3.0m^2$, but depending on location, position and shape of the chimney or duct, may have to be of larger dimensions as shown in **Figures 8A, 8B and 8C**. The dimensions shown are the minimum required for the necessary size of working area. For small vertical ducts the provision of an L-shaped platform may satisfy more easily the requirement of necessary working area as an alternative to the design shown in **Figure 8A**.

4.3 Sampling platforms installed for use at sample planes located in a horizontal section of a duct or flue, should not depart from the requirements previously laid down for sampling planes located in sections of vertical ducts under 4.1 and 4.2 above. However, where the selected sample plane is located in a horizontal section of a large size duct or flue, and where some of the sample points are positioned above a convenient and safe working height (nominally 1750mm maximum for sample probe handling), it will be necessary to provide a dual level sampling platform of adequate design so that sampling staff can carry out the full range of sampling requirements in a safe and satisfactory manner.

Figure 8 Sampling platforms - working area and orientation requirements

Figure 8A Platform recommendations for small vertical circular ducts (<3600mm diameter)

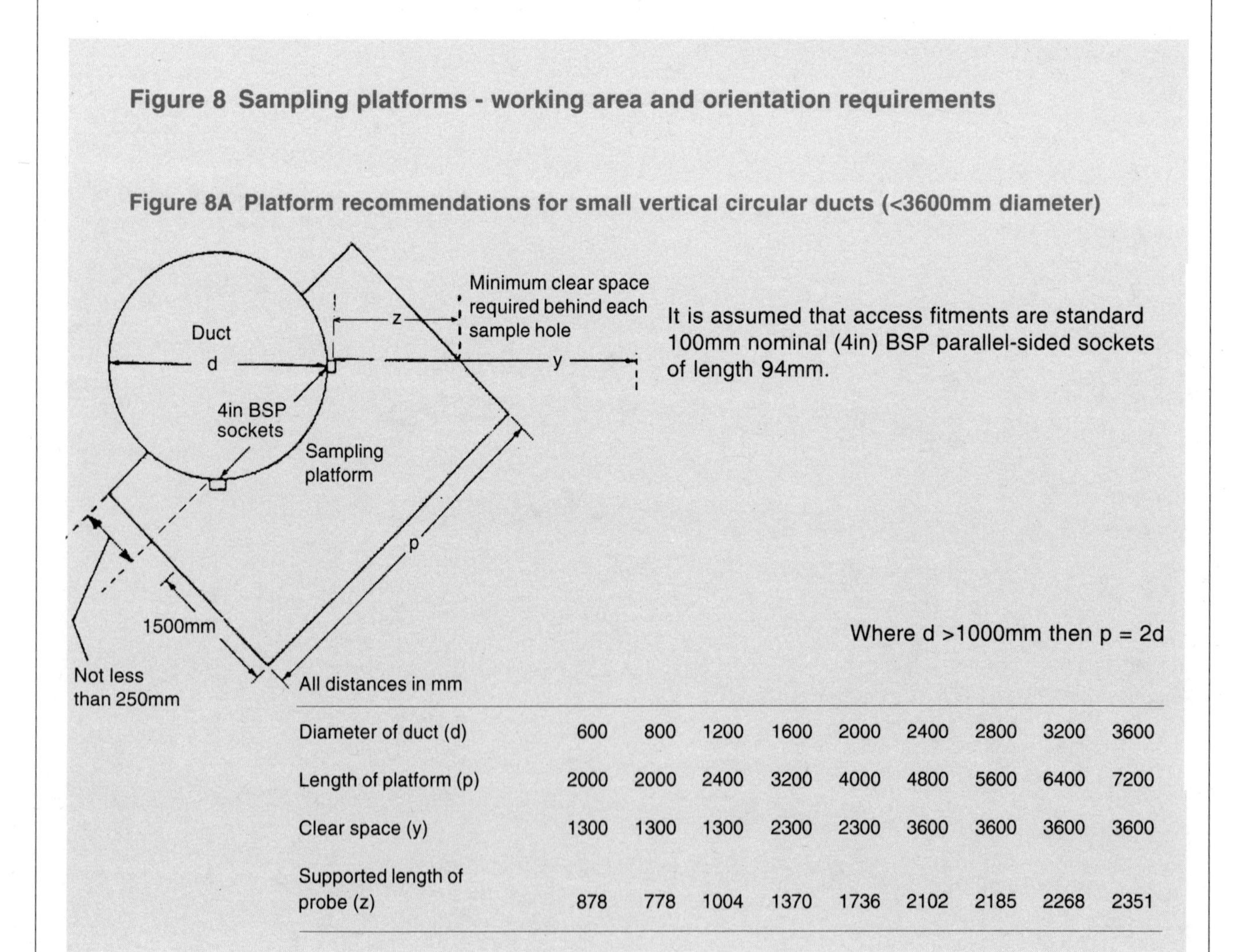

Diameter of duct (d)	600	800	1200	1600	2000	2400	2800	3200	3600
Length of platform (p)	2000	2000	2400	3200	4000	4800	5600	6400	7200
Clear space (y)	1300	1300	1300	2300	2300	3600	3600	3600	3600
Supported length of probe (z)	878	778	1004	1370	1736	2102	2185	2268	2351

Figure 8B Platform recommendations for large vertical circular ducts (over 3600mm diameter)

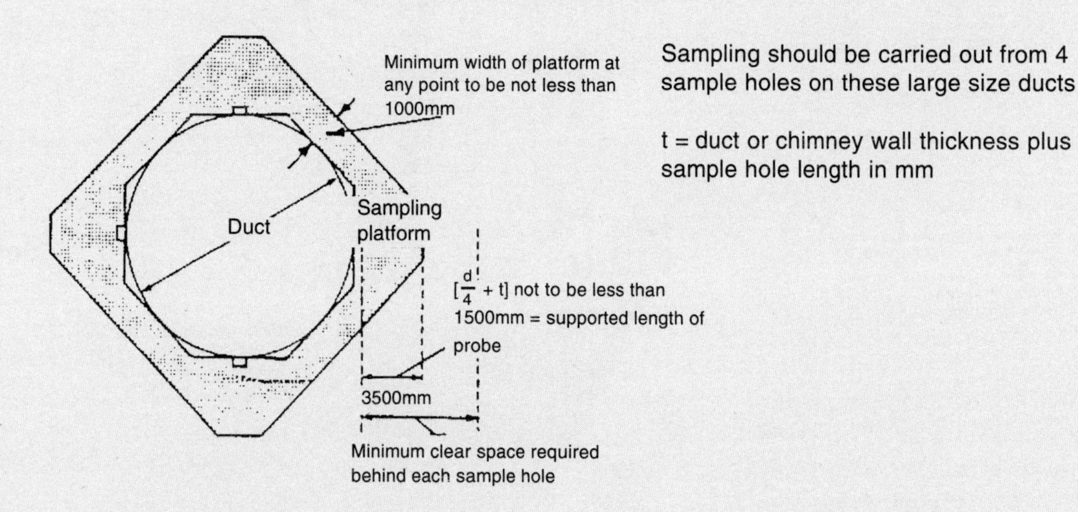

Figure 8C Platform recommendations for small and medium sized vertical, square and rectangular ducts (up to L = 3600mm)

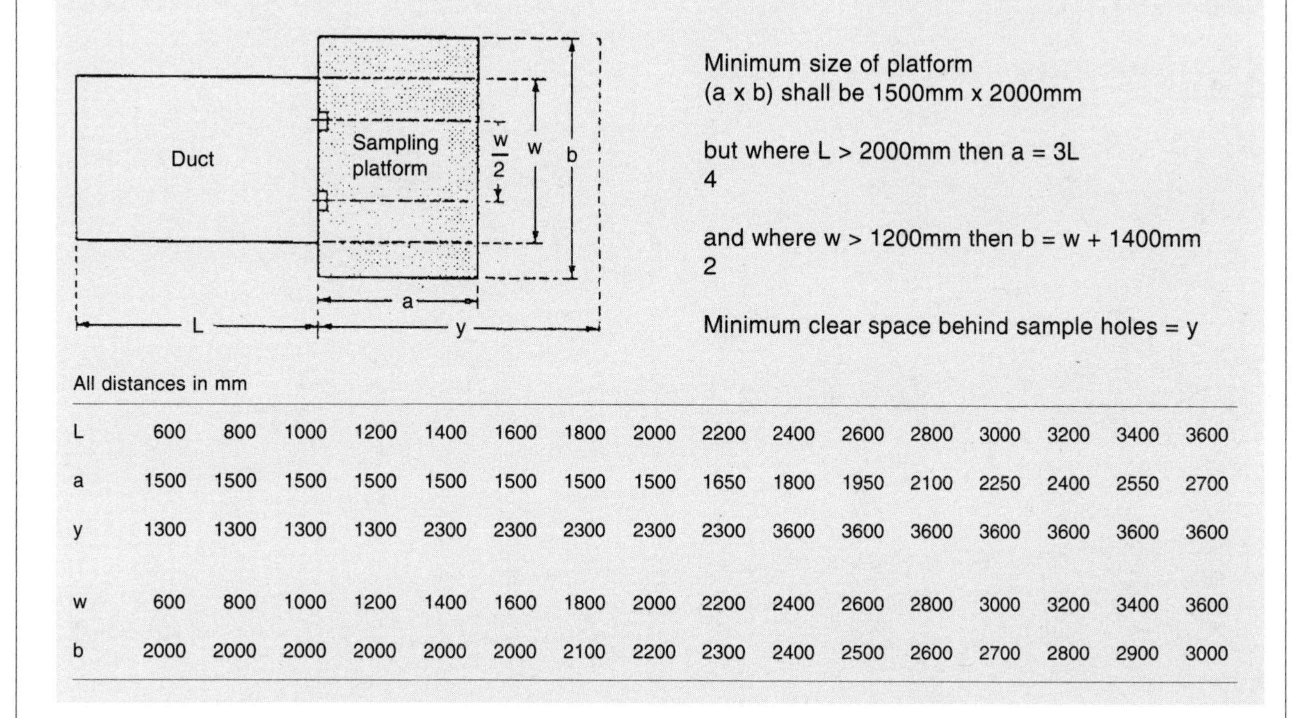

All distances in mm

L	600	800	1000	1200	1400	1600	1800	2000	2200	2400	2600	2800	3000	3200	3400	3600
a	1500	1500	1500	1500	1500	1500	1500	1500	1650	1800	1950	2100	2250	2400	2550	2700
y	1300	1300	1300	1300	2300	2300	2300	2300	2300	3600	3600	3600	3600	3600	3600	3600
w	600	800	1000	1200	1400	1600	1800	2000	2200	2400	2600	2800	3000	3200	3400	3600
b	2000	2000	2000	2000	2000	2000	2100	2200	2300	2400	2500	2600	2700	2800	2900	3000

5.0 Service Requirements

5.1 A 110v single phase power supply should be available on the sampling platform, preferably fitted with weatherproof outlets to *BS 4343:1968.* Where a supply of 110v power is not readily available, the use of a portable isolating transformer connected directly to a 240v outlet is an acceptable alternative. (See the *Electricity at Work Regulations 1989 SI No 635*)

5.2 Where it is necessary to sample emissions to atmosphere on sites where flammable substances are present as a hazard, electric motors or other uncertified electrical equipment must not be used, unless the works management makes special provisions and gives direct authority to do so.

Compressed air or water powered ejectors can be used as an alternative for the withdrawing of samples from ducts or chimneys, where appropriate.

5.3 Adequate lighting is essential on all sampling platforms and supplementary lighting may be required to serve platforms in dark or remote locations.

5.4 Shelter or protection from the elements may also be required in exceptional circumstances or where the sample platform is in a very exposed position.

6.0 Access to Sampling Platforms

6.1 The sampling platform, sampling platform access and the approaches to it, should be kept clean and free from accumulations of deposits, or site debris. The platform should be self draining and free from standing water. This is especially important for ladder approaches and in wet weather conditions.

NB The requirements of safety, in relation to the sampling of emissions to atmosphere from ducted sources, are not directly addressed in these notes. The assessment of all safety matters, general and site specific, should be undertaken as a separate exercise prior to the commencement of any sampling operations. See also Appendix.

List of Figures and Graphs

Appendix

BIBLIOGRAPHY

The items listed in this bibliography are not definitive on any of the subjects included, but are intended to serve as a general guide to the information available.

More information is available from sources such as the Health & Safety Executive (HSE), RoSPA (Royal Society for the Prevention of Accidents), British Standards, ISO (International Standards Organisation), etc., in the form of Codes of Practice, Guidance Notes, and Advice from Industry. In the event of specific safety requirements arising, eg. for a particular chemical hazard or an up-date of Regulations etc., a literature search would be necessary.

General

1. Departmental safety policy of the Departments of the Environment and Transport. Appendix to EB 224/89. 10 March 1989.

2. HSE. General legal requirements, 1988. Summary Sheet for Small Contractors, SS1.

Access and Scaffolds etc.

AS/1 HSE. General access scaffolds, 1988. Summary Sheet for Small Contractors, SS3.

AS/2 HSE. General access scaffolds, 1982. Guidance Note GS/15. HMSO, ISBN 0 11 883545 9.

AS/3 HSE. Tower scaffolds, 1987. Guidance Note GS/42. HMSO, ISBN 0 11 883941 1.

AS/4 HSE. Suspended access equipment, 1983. Guidance Note PM/30. HMSO, ISBN 0 11 883577 7.

AS/5 HSE. Tower scaffolds, 1988. Summary Sheet for Small Contractors, SS10.

AS/6 DD 72:1981 Design requirements for access and working scaffolds. British Standards.

AS/7 BS 1139 Metal scaffolding. BS 1139:Part 3:1983 Specification for prefabricated access and working towers.

AS/8 BS 5973:1990 Code of practice for access and working scaffolds and special scaffold structures in steel.

AS/9 BS 5974:1990 Code of practice for temporarily installed suspended scaffolds and access equipment.

Electrical Safety

ES/1 The Electricity at Work Regulations 1989. SI No 635. HMSO, ISBN 0 11 096635 X.

ES/2 HSE. Memorandum of guidance on the Electricity at Work Regulations 1989. HS(R) 25. HMSO, ISBN 0 11 883963 2.

ES/3 HSE. The safe use of portable electrical apparatus (electrical safety), 1990. Guidance Note PM 32. HMSO, ISBN 0 11 885590 5.

ES/4 HSE. Selection and use of electric handlamps, 1984. Guidance Note PM 38. HMSO, 0 11 883582 3.

ES/5 HSE. Electricity on construction sites 1983. Guidance Note GS 24. HMSO, ISBN 0 11 883570 X.

ES/6 HSE. Protection against electric shock, 1984. Guidance Note GS 27. HMSO, ISBN 0 11 883583 1.

ES/7 HSE. Flexible leads, plugs, sockets etc., 1985. Guidance Note GS 37. HMSO, ISBN 0 11 883519 X

ES/8 HSE. Electrical apparatus for use in potentially explosive atmospheres, 1984. Guidance Booklet HS(G) 22. HMSO, 0 11 883746 X.

ES/9 BS EN 60529:1991 Specification for degrees of protection provided by enclosures (IP Code).

Environmental Hygiene

EH/1 HSE. Legionnaire's disease, 1989 IAC/L27.

EH/2 HSE. Monitoring strategies for toxic substances, 1989. Guidance Note EH 42. HMSO, ISBN 0 11 885412 7.

EH/3 HSE. Occupational exposure limits. Guidance Note EH 40. Revised edition published each year. HMSO, ISBN 0 11 885580 8.

Ladders and Stairways

LS/1 HSE. Safe use of ladders, 1988. Summary Sheet for Small Contractors, SS2.

LS/2 HSE. Safe use of ladders, step ladders and trestles, 1984. Guidance Note GS 31. HMSO, ISBN 0 11 883594 7.

LS/3 Factory stairways, ladders and handrails. Engineering Equipment & Materials Users Association Handbook.

LS/4 Timber ladders. RoSPA Pamphlet 5.

LS/5 BS 2037:1990 Specification for portable aluminium ladders, steps, trestles and lightweight stagings.

LS/6 BS 4211:1987 Specification for ladders for permanent access to chimneys, other high structures, silos and bins.

LS/7 BS 5395 Ladders and walkways

BS 5395 Part 1:1977 (1984) Code of practice for the design of straight stairs.

BS 5395 Part 2:1984 Code of practice for the design of helical and spiral stairs.

BS 5395 Part 3:1985 Code of practice for the design of industrial type stairs, permanent ladders and walkways.

Mobile Platforms

MP/1 Mobile elevating work platforms - user safety guide. Construction Plant Hire Association.

MP/2 HSE. Safety in working with power operated mobile work platforms, 1982. HS(G) 19. HMSO, ISBN 0 11 883628 5.

MP/3 BS 6289 Work platforms.

BS 6289 Part 1:1982 Code of practice for mobile scissor operated work platforms.

MP/4 BS 7171:1989 Specification for mobile elevating work platforms.

Protective Clothing

PC/1 HSE. General legal requirements, 1988. Summary Sheet for Small Contractors, SS1 (Also General 1)

PC/2 Protection of hearing at work. Confederation of British Industry.

PC/3 Reference book of protective equipment. Industrial Safety (Protective Equipment) Manufacturers' Association.

Ropes

R/1 BS 2052:1989 Specification for ropes made from manila, sisal, hemp, cotton and coir.

R/2 BS 4928:1985 Specification for man-made fibre ropes.

HMIP PUBLICATIONS

Chief Inspector's Guidance Notes

Industry Sector Guidance Notes

Guidance Note IPR1 Fuel and Power Industry Sector, £4.50 ISBN 0-11-752408-5

Guidance Note IPR2 Metal Industry Sector, £4.15 ISBN 0-11-752409-3

Guidance Note IPR3 Mineral Industry Sector, £3.80 ISBN 0-11-752410-7

Guidance Note IPR4 Chemical Industry Sector, £4.15 ISBN 0-11-752411-5

Guidance Note IPR5 Waste Disposal Industry Sector, £3.80 ISBN 0-11-752412-3

Process Guidance Notes

Fuel and Power Sector

IPR1/1 Combustion Processes. Large Boilers and Furnaces 50MW(th) and Over, £5.00 ISBN 0-11-752439-5

IPR1/2 Combustion Processes. Gas Turbines, £4.65 ISBN 0-11-752569-3

IPR1/3 Combustion Processes. Compression Ignition Engines 50MW(th) and Over, £4.65 ISBN 0-11-752570-7

IPR1/4 Combustion Processes. Waste and Recovered Oil Burners 3MW(th) and Over, £5.15 ISBN 0-11-752571-5

IPR1/5 Combustion Processes. Combustion of Solid Fuel Manufactured from Municipal Waste in Appliances with a Net Rated Thermal Input of 3 Megawatts or More, £5.15 ISBN 0-11-752572-3

IPR1/6 Combustion Processes. Combustion of Fuel Manufactured from or Comprised of Tyres, Tyre Rubber or Similar Rubber Waste in Appliances with a Net Rated Thermal Input of 3MW or More, £4.65 ISBN 0-11-752573-1

IPR1/7 Combusion Processes. Combustion of Solid Fuel Manufactured from or Comprised of Poultry Litter in Appliances with a Net Rated Thermal Input of 3MW or More, £4.65 ISBN 0-11-752574-X

IPR1/8 Combustion Processes. Combustion of Solid Fuel which is Manufactured from or is Comprised of Wood Waste or Straw in Appliances with a Net Rated Thermal Input of 3MW or More, £4.65 ISBN 0-11-752575-8

IPR1/9 Carbonisation and Associated Processes. Coke Manufacture, £5.70 ISBN 0-11-752576-6

IPR1/10 Carbonisation and Associated Processes. Smokeless Fuel, Activated Carbon and Carbon Black Manufacture, £5.70 ISBN 0-11-752577-4

IPR1/11 Gasification Processes. Gasification of Solid and Liquid Feedstocks, £5.15 ISBN 0-11-752578-2

IPR1/12 Gasification Processes. Refining of Natural Gas, £5.70 ISBN 0-11-752579-0

IPR1/13 Gasification Processes. The Refining of Natural Gas at Liquefied Natural Gas Sites, £4.30 ISBN 0-11-752580-4

IPR1/14 Gasification Processes. The Odorising of Natural Gas or Liquefied Petroleum Gas, £3.95 ISBN 0-11-752581-2

IPR1/15 Petroleum Processes. Crude Oil Refineries, £7.50 ISBN 0-11-752582-0

IPR1/16 Petroleum Processes. On-Shore Oil Production, £4.65 ISBN 0-11-752583-9

IPR1/17 Combustion Processes. Reheat and Heat Treatment Furnaces, £4.65 ISBN 0-11-752584-7

Waste Disposal and Recycling Sector

IPR5/1 Merchant & In House Chemical Waste Incineration, £5.15 ISBN 0-11-752653-3

IPR5/2 Clinical Waste Incineration, £5.15 ISBN 0-11-752652-5

IPR5/3 Municipal Waste Incineration, £5.70 ISBN 0-11-752649-5

IPR5/4 Animal Carcass Incineration, £5.15 ISBN 0-11-752654-1

IPR5/5 The Burning out of Metal Containers, £4.65 ISBN 0-11-752651-7

IPR5/6 Making Solid Fuel from Waste, £4.65 ISBN 0-11-752647-9

IPR5/7 Cleaning & Regeneration of Carbon, £5.15 ISBN 0-11-752655-X

IPR5/8 Recovery of Organic Solvents by Distillation, £5.15 ISBN 0-11-752645-2

IPR5/9 Regeneration of Ion Exchange Resins, £4.30 ISBN 0-11-752650-9

IPR5/10 Recovery of Oil by Distillation, £5.15 ISBN 0-11-752648-7

IPR5/11 Sewage Sludge Incineration, £5.15 ISBN 0-11-752646-0

Mineral Industry Sector

IPR3/1 Cement Manufacture and Associated Processes, £5.70 ISBN 0-11-752681-9

IPR3/2 Lime Manufacture and Associated Processes, £5.15 ISBN 0-11-752682-7

IPR3/3 Processes Involving Asbestos, £5.15 ISBN 0-11-752683-5

IPR3/4 Glass Fibres & Non-Asbestos Mineral Fibres, £5.15 ISBN 0-11-752684-3

IPR3/5 Glass Manufacture and Production. Glass Frit and Enamel Frit, £5.15 ISBN 0-11-752685

IPR3/6 Ceramic Processes, £5.15 ISBN 0-11-752686-X

Chemical Industry Sector

IPR4/1 Petrochemical Processes, £8.50 ISBN 0-11-752738-6

IPR4/2 Processes for the Production and Use of Amines, Nitriles, Isocyanates and Pyridines, £9 ISBN 0-11-752739-4

IPR4/3 Processes for the Production or Use of Acetylene, Aldehydes etc., £8.50 ISBN 0-11-752740-8

IPR4/4 Processes for the Production or Use of Organic Sulphur Compounds, and Production, Use or Recovery of Carbon Disulphide, £8.65 ISBN 0-11-752741-6

IPR4/5 Batch Manufacture of Organic Chemicals in Multipurpose Plant, £8 ISBN 0-11-752742-4

IPR4/6 Production and Polymerisation of Organic Monomers, £10 ISBN 0-11-752743-2

IPR4/7 Processes for the Manufacture of Organo-Metallic Compounds, £7.70 ISBN 0-11-752744-0

IPR4/8 Pesticide Processes, £7.50 ISBN 0-11-752745-9

IPR4/9 Pharmaceutical Processes, £8.50 ISBN 0-11-752746-7

Due for publication May 1993:

IPR4/10 Processes for the Manufacture, Use or Release of Oxides of Sulphur and the Manufacture, Recovery, Condensation or Distillation of Sulphuric Acid or Oleum

IPR4/11 Processes for the Manufacture or Recovery of Nitric Acid and Processes Involving the Manufacture or Release of Acid-forming Oxides of Nitrogen

IPR4/12 Processes for the Sulphonation or Nitration of Organic Chemicals

IPR4/13 Processes for the Manufacture of, or which Use or Release Halogens, Mixed Halogen Compounds or Oxhalocompounds

IPR4/14 Processes for the Manufacture of, or which Use or Release Hydrogen Halides or any of their Acids

IPR4/15 Processes for the Halogenation of Organic Chemicals

IPR4/16 Processes for the Manufacture of Chemical Fertilizers or their Conversion into Granules

IPR4/17 Bulk storage installations

Guidance Notes for processes contained in the remaining sectors will be published progressively before they become subject to integrated pollution control. More details from Rm 163, Technical Guidance Branch, Government Buildings, Burghill Road, Westbury-on-Trym, Bristol BS10 6EZ

Protecting Britain's Environment: the work of Her Majesty's Inspectorate of Pollution

Available free of charge from DOE, PO Box 151, London E15 2HF, Fax 0181 533 1618

RELEVANT DOE PUBLICATIONS

Processes Prescribed for Air Pollution Control by Local Authorities: Secretary of State's Guidance

PG1/1(91) Waste Oil Burners. Less than 0.4MW net rated thermal input, £3.40 ISBN 0 11 752407 7

PG1/2(91) Waste Oil or Recovered Oil Burners. Less than 3MW net rated thermal input, £2.70 ISBN 0 11 752405 0

PG1/3(91) Boilers and Furnaces. 20–50MW net rated thermal input, £2.70 ISBN 0 11 752384 4

PG1/4(91) Gas Turbines. 20–50MW net rated thermal input, £2.70 ISBN 0 11 752392 5

PG1/5(91) Compression Ignition Engines. 20–50MW net rated thermal input, £2.70 ISBN 0 11 752389 5

PG1/6(91) Tyre and Rubber Combustion Processes between 0.4 and 3MW net rated thermal input, £2.70 ISBN 0 11 752404 2

PG1/7(91) Straw Combustion Processes between 0.4 and 3MW net rated thermal input, £2.70 ISBN 0 11 752401 8

PG1/8(91) Wood Combustion Processes between 0.4 and 3MW net rated thermal input, £2.70 ISBN 0 11 752406 9

PG1/9(91) Poultry Litter Combustion Processes between 0.4 and 3MW net rated thermal input, £2.70 ISBN 0 11 752399 2

PG1/10(92) Waste Derived Fuel Combustion Processes less than 3MW, £3.45 ISBN 0 11 752594 4

PG1/11(92) Reheat and Heat Treatment Furnaces. 20–50MW net rated thermal input, £2.75 ISBN 0 11 752670 3

PG2/1(91) Furnaces for the Extraction of Non-ferrous Metal from Scrap, £2.70 ISBN 0 11 752398 4

PG2/2(91) Hot Dip Galvanising Processes, £3.40 ISBN 0 11 752479 4

PG2/3(91) Electrical and Rotary Furnaces, £2.70 ISBN 0 11 752476 X

PG2/4(91) Iron, Steel and Non-ferrous Metal Foundry Processes, £3.30 ISBN 0 11 752478 6

PG2/5(91) Hot and Cold Blast Cupolas, £2.70 ISBN 0 11 752474 3

PG2/6(91) Aluminium and Aluminium Alloy Processes, £2.70 ISBN 0 11 752467 0

PG2/7(91) Zinc and Zinc Alloy Processes, £2.70 ISBN 0 11 752460 3

PG2/8(91) Copper and Copper Alloy Processes, £2.70 ISBN 0 11 752473 5

PG2/9(91) Metal Decontamination Processes, £2.70 ISBN 0 11 752481 6

PG3/1(91) Blending, Packing, Loading and Use of Bulk Cement, £1.90 ISBN 0 11 752385 2

PG3/2(91) Manufacture of Heavy Clay Goods and Refractory Goods, £3.70 ISBN 0 11 752386 0

PG3/3(91) Glass (excluding Lead Glass) Manufacturing Processes, £2.70 ISBN 0-11-752394-1

PG3/4(91) Lead Glass Manufacturing Processes, £2.70 ISBN 0-11-752393-3

PG3/5(91) Coal, Coke and Coal Product Processes, £2.70 ISBN 0-11-752469-7

PG3/6(91) Processes for the Polishing or Etching of Glass or Glass Products using Hydrofluoric Acid, £2.70 ISBN 0-11-752395-X

PG3/7(91) Exfoliation of Vermiculite and Expansion of Perlite, £2.70 ISBN 0-11-752459-X

PG3/8(91) Quarry Processes including Roadstone Plants and the Size Reduction of Bricks, Tiles and Concrete, £3.40 ISBN 0-11-752463-8

PG3/9(91) Sand Drying and Cooling, £2.70 ISBN 0-11-752464-6

PG3/10(91) China and Ball Clay, £2.70 ISBN 0-11-752470-0

PG3/11(91) Spray Drying of Ceramic Materials, £2.70 ISBN 0-11-752468-9

PG3/12(91) Plaster Processes, £2.70 ISBN 0-11-752458-1

PG3/13(91) Asbestos Processes, £3.40 ISBN 0-11-752482-4

PG3/14(91) Lime Slaking Processes, £1.90 ISBN 0-11-752480-8

PG5/1(91) Clinical Waste Incineration Processes under 1 tonne an hour (second (revised)) edition, £3.45 ISBN 0-11-752688-6

PG5/2(91) Crematoria, £2.70 ISBN 0-11-752390-9

PG5/3(91) Animal Carcase Incineration Processes under 1 tonne an hour, £2.70 ISBN 0-11-752383-6

PG5/4(91) General Waste Incineration Processes under 1 tonne an hour, £2.70 ISBN 0-11-752397-6

PG5/5(91) Sewage Sludge Incineration Processes £2.70 ISBN 0-11-752400-X

PG6/1(91) Animal By Product Rendering, £2.70 ISBN 0-11-752461-1

PG6/2(91) Manufacture of Timber and Wood-based Products, £1.90 ISBN 0-11-752403-4

PG6/3(91) Chemical Treatment of Timber and Wood-based Products, £2.70 ISBN 0-11-752402-6

PG6/4(91) Processes for the Manufacture of Particleboard and Fibreboard, £2.70 ISBN 0-11-752387-9

PG6/5(91) Maggot Breeding Processes, £3.40 ISBN 0-11-752396-8

PG6/6(91) Fur Breeding Processes, £2.70 ISBN 0-11-752391-7

PG6/7(91) Printing and Coating of Metal Packaging, £3.75 ISBN 0-11-752462-X

PG6/8(91) Textile and Fabric Coating and Finishing Processes, £3.40 ISBN 0-11-752466-2

PG6/9(91) Manufacture of Coating Powder, £1.90 ISBN 0-11-752471-9

PG6/10(92) Coating Manufacturing, £3.45 ISBN 0-11-752595-2

PG6/11(92) Manufacture of Printing Ink, £2.75 ISBN 0-11-752596-0

PG6/12(91) Production of Natural Sausage Casings, Tripe, Chitterlings and other Boiled Green Offal Products, £1.90 ISBN 0-11-752465-4

PG6/13(91) Coil Coating Processes, £3.40 ISBN 0-11-752472-7

PG6/14(91) Film Coating Processes, £3.40 ISBN 0-11-752477-8

PG6/15(91) Coating in Drum Manufacturing and Reconditioning Processes, £3.75 ISBN 0-11-752475-1

PG6/16(92) Printworks, £1.75 ISBN 0-11 752597-9

PG6/17(92) Printing of Flexible Packaging, £2.75 ISBN 0-11-752598-7

PG6/18(92) Paper Coating, £2.75 ISBN 0-11-752599-5

PG6/19(92) Fish Meal and Fish Oil, £2.75 ISBN 0-11-752600-2

PG6/20(92) Paint Application in Vehicle Manufacturing, £3.90 ISBN 0-11-752601-0

PG6/21(92) Hide and Skin Processes, £2.75 ISBN 0-11-752602-9

PG6/22(92) Leather Finishing, £2.75
ISBN 0 11 752603 7

PG6/23(92) Coating of Metal and Plastic, £4.35
ISBN 0 11 752604 5

PG6/24(92) Pet Food Manufacturing, £2.75
ISBN 0 11 752605 3

PG6/25(92) Vegetable Oil Extractiona and Fat and Oil Refining, £2.75 ISBN 0 11 752606 1

PG6/26(92) Animal Feed Compounding, £2.75
ISBN 0 11 752607 X

PG6/27(92) Vegetable Matter Drying, £2.75
ISBN 0 11 752608 8

PG6/28(92) Rubber Processes, £3.85
ISBN 0 11 752609 6

PG6/29(92) Di-isocyanate Processes, £1.95
ISBN 0 11 752610 X

PG6/30(92) Production of Compost for Mushrooms, £2.75 ISBN 0 11 752611 8

PG6/31(92) Powder Coating (including Sheradizing), £2.75 ISBN 0 11 752612 6

PG6/32(92) Adhesive Coating, £4.35
ISBN 0 11 752613 4

PG6/33(92) Wood Coating, £3.90
ISBN 0 11 752614 2

PG6/34(92) Respraying of Road Vehicles, £3.45
ISBN 0 11 752615 0

PG6/35(92) Metal and other Thermal Spraying Processes, £2.75 ISBN 0 11 752616 9

PG6/36(92) Tobacco Processing, £2.75
ISBN 0 11 752617 7

PG6/37(92) Knackers Yards, £1.95
ISBN 0 11 752618 5

PG6/38(92) Blood Processing, £1.95
ISBN 0 11 752619 3

PG6/39(92) Animal By-product Dealers, £1.95
ISBN 0 11 752620 7

UG-1 May 1992 Secretary of State's Guidance – Revisions/Additions to Existing Process and General Guidance Notes: No 1, £4.35 ISBN 0 11 752661 4

Printed in the United Kingdom for HMSO
Dd301238 8/95 C9 G3397 10170